GW00568141

say Eh-oh!

Time for...

This Teletubbies Annual 2002 belongs to

I am the scary Lion
And I'm looking for the Bear.
I know she's hiding
But I don't know where!

First published in 2001 by BBC Worldwide Ltd
Woodlands, 80 Wood Lane, London, W12 OTT
Text from original TV scripts by Andrew Davenport
Text, design and illustrations © 2001 BBC Worldwide Ltd
Teletubbies characters and logo © and ™ 1996 Ragdoll Ltd
Licensed by BBC Worldwide Ltd
ISBN 0 563 476427

Editor Ruth Paley
Designer Lisa White
Sub-Editor John Tomlinson

Colour reproduction by Polestar Digital Ltd, Watford
Printed and bound by Proost Nv, Turnhout, Belgium
Illustrated by Jane Swift/SGA.
Photography pages 14-15 and 48 by Christopher Baines and page 49 by Chris Capstick.

Thank you to the following children who were photographed for this book: Tabatha, Rachael, Gabriel and Dante.

The Bear is hiding in the book. Can you find her?

Jumping Over

One day in Teletubbyland, Tinky Winky jumped over his bag.

Eh-oh!

Boing!

One... two... three... Jump!

'Ray! Tinky Winky jump over bag!

One day in Teletubbyland, Dipsy jumped over the flowers.

One... two... three... Jump!

Jump!

Jump!

Boing!

Wheee!

Boing!

8

The Teletubbies love jumping.

And Teletubbies love each other very much!

Teletubbies jump!

The Teletubbies love jumping! Who jumped over what in the story? Finish these pictures by drawing one of the Teletubbies jumping over each thing.

When you've finished – jump up in the air!

11

Little Miss Muffet

Read the rhyme to Laa-Laa.
Oh dear! The pictures are all mixed
up. Which picture should come first,
which one is in the middle and which
one comes last?

Little Miss Muffet sat on a tuffet
There came a big spider who sat
and frightened Miss Muffet away

Uh-oh!

ping

eating her curds and whey.
own beside her

13

Come and see

Hello! We are going outside.

We are feeding the swans.

The swans eat lots of bread.

I like eating bread, too!

Bye-bye!

We love the swans very much. Bye-bye!

15

Colouring-in

Bo Peep

One day in Teletubbyland, something appeared from far away...

Baaa!

Baaa!

Baaa!

Baaa!

Baaa!

18

Baaa!

Baaa!

Baaa!

Oh, lovely sheep! There you are!

Come along, sheep!

Bye-bye!

21

Funny noises

Join in with the Teletubbies and make these funny noises!

Slurpy slurp!

Splurt splurt!

Crunch munch!

Moo moooooo!

Snuffly snore!

Who dropped what?
Match each Teletubby
to what they have lost,
by drawing a line.

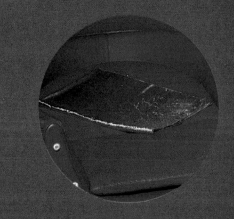

23

The golden and silver tree

One day in Teletubbyland, Laa-Laa was out for a walk when something appeared from far away.

"Oooh!" said Laa-Laa. "What's that?"

It was a golden tree.

"Oh, golden tree!" said Laa-Laa.

Then Laa-Laa heard a lovely tinkling noise. One by one, silver leaves appeared on the branches of the golden tree.

What a beautiful gold and silver tree!

"What a beautiful gold and silver tree!" said

Laa-Laa.

Tinky Winky, Dipsy and Po came to see the tree. They thought the gold and silver tree was very beautiful.

"Oooh! Gold and silver tree very beautiful!" said Tinky Winky, Dipsy and Po.

And then the gold and silver tree disappeared...
'Ping!'

"Ow!" said the Teletubbies. "All gone!"

The Teletubbies love the beautiful gold and silver tree, and they love each other very much.

Big Hug!

25

Animal parade

One day in Teletubbyland, the animals appeared. Point to the four differences between these two pictures.

27

The Noo-noo tidies up Tinky-Winky's bag and Dipsy's hat

One day in Teletubbyland, Dipsy was wearing his hat.

Eh-oh!

Dipsy hat!

Dipsy loves his hat!

Eh-oh!

Tinky Winky was carrying his bag.

Eh-oh Tinky Winky!

Eh-oh Dipsy!

Can you see me?

Then Tinky Winky...

...put Dipsy's hat inside his bag!

Dipsy was very surprised!

Hat in bag! Oh no!

Then the Noo-noo came along.

Hat inside bag!

Naughty Noo-noo!

Naughty Noo-noo!

The Noo-noo was very full with a hat and bag inside him.

Shlurrp!

So out came the hat.

Dipsy was very happy to have his hat back.

Then out came the bag. Tinky Winky was very happy to have his bag back.

Shlurrrp!

Tinky Winky love bag!

Dipsy love hat!

Tinky Winky and Dipsy love the hat and bag.

And Teletubbies love each other very much.

Big Hug!

The Noo-noo tidie

What is the Noo-noo about to tidy up?
Join up the dots to find out!

sucky sucky sluuuurp

35

The Noo-noo tidie

Who has made such a mess? Follow the custard footprints to find out!

Help the Noo-noo tidy up by drawing a ring round all the tubby custard splats and tubby toast in the picture.

slurpy slurp! slurpy slurp!

The Teletubbies hold the balloon

1

2

4

5

One day in Teletubbyland...
Can you finish the story?

Here comes Po

Draw a line with a pencil to show Po the way back to the house. Make sure she doesn't ride over any flowers and that she passes all the other Teletubbies on the way.

Don't tread on us!

Crunch crunch!

See-saw

One day in Teletubbyland, something appeared from far away.

ping

Oooh! What's that?

It was a see-saw.

See-saw!

Dipsy and Laa-Laa played on the see-saw.

Dipsy and Laa-Laa liked playing on the see-saw.

Laa-Laa see-saw!

They told Tinky Winky and Po about the see-saw.

They showed Tinky Winky and Po how to play on the see-saw.

44

Then it was the turn of Tinky Winky and Po to play on the see-saw.

Uh-oh!

But Tinky Winky was too heavy to play on the see-saw with Po.

Dipsy and Laa-Laa help!

So Dipsy and Laa-Laa helped Tinky Winky and Po.

See-saw, Marjory Daw
Johnny shall have
a new master...

He shall have
but a penny a day
because he can't work
any faster.

The Teletubbies
love playing on
the see-saw.

Favourite things

teddy bears' picnic

pushing my pram